STAINED GLASS
COLORING BOOK

FLOWER DESIGNS

nk you for purchasing this coloring book! We hope that you enjoy coloring it as much as we enjoyed creating it. Please consider leaving a review, we really appreciate hearing your opinion!

Sign-Up to Get a Free Coloring Book

ıbscribe to our newsletter and get a free printable coloring book of some of our most popular illustrations. Plus you'll receive special offers, sneak peeks at new releases, and more.
Visit us at **www.creativecoloring.co** for details.

We want to hear from you!

'e hope you've enjoyed this coloring book and that is brings you many hours of fun, stress relief, and creativity. We'd love to see and share your creations.

Send us your ideas, suggestions, and finished artwork:

www.creativecoloring.co
facebook.com/creativecoloringpress
Instagram: @creativecoloringpress
Twitter: @creativecoloringpress

Printed in Great Britain
by Amazon